Piano
Scales & Arpeggios
ABRSM Grade 3
from **2009**

Why practise scales?

Welcome to this book of scales and arpeggios for Grade 3 Piano. Scale practice plays an essential part in developing a pianist's skills, and time devoted to these exercises within each practice session will improve keyboard fluency. Not only can many areas of piano technique be developed through scale practice (such as posture, hand position, co-ordination, balance between the hands and movement of the arm), but the sense of key and pattern acquired through familiarity with scales and arpeggios has several benefits: it speeds up the learning of new pieces, develops evenness of line and quality of tone, builds aural awareness, and increases familiarity with the geography of the piano.

About this book

The printed pitches have been chosen primarily for ease of reading and the starting notes may not always be in the most appropriate or comfortable octave(s). Candidates are therefore free to start in a different octave as long as the required range is covered.

The printed rhythmic groupings are not compulsory; of overriding importance is that the requirements are played with rhythmic evenness and without undue accentuation.

For the exam

Tempo

The given metronome marks indicate *minimum* recommended speeds and serve as a guide to the expectations of the examiner. Experienced teachers will know what their candidates are able to achieve safely, although it is important to avoid accurate yet laboured playing which shows that the scale or arpeggio has been memorized but lacks the finger facility that is such an important part of developing technique.

Fingering

The suggested fingerings in this book are neither obligatory nor exhaustive; any practical and systematic fingering that produces a good result will be accepted in the exam. Some alternative fingering is shown as follows: 4/3. The decision as to which fingering to adopt will depend on the size and shape of the player's hand, and candidates should experiment to find solutions that work for them. (Examiners will not comment on the choice of fingering, unless it interferes with the performance.)

On the day

All requirements must be played from memory. Examiners will usually ask for at least one of each type of scale or arpeggio required at the grade.

The examiner will be looking for:
- a positive sense of rhythm without undue accentuation
- even, firm tone and a musical curve
- good legato
- accurate and fluent realization of the different types of scales and arpeggios
- convincing negotiation of technical challenges such as smooth passage of the thumb and hand co-ordination.

Reference must always be made to the syllabus for the year in which the exam is to be taken, in case any changes have been made to the requirements.

General information on the exam can be found in *Exam Information & Regulations*, and in the guide for candidates, teachers and parents, *These Music Exams*. These and the syllabus document are available online at www.abrsm.org, as well as free of charge from music retailers, from ABRSM local representatives or from the Services Department, ABRSM, 24 Portland Place, London W1B 1LU, United Kingdom.

MAJOR SCALES

hands together one octave apart and hands separately

two octaves ♩ = 80

A major

E major

B major

B♭ major

E♭ major

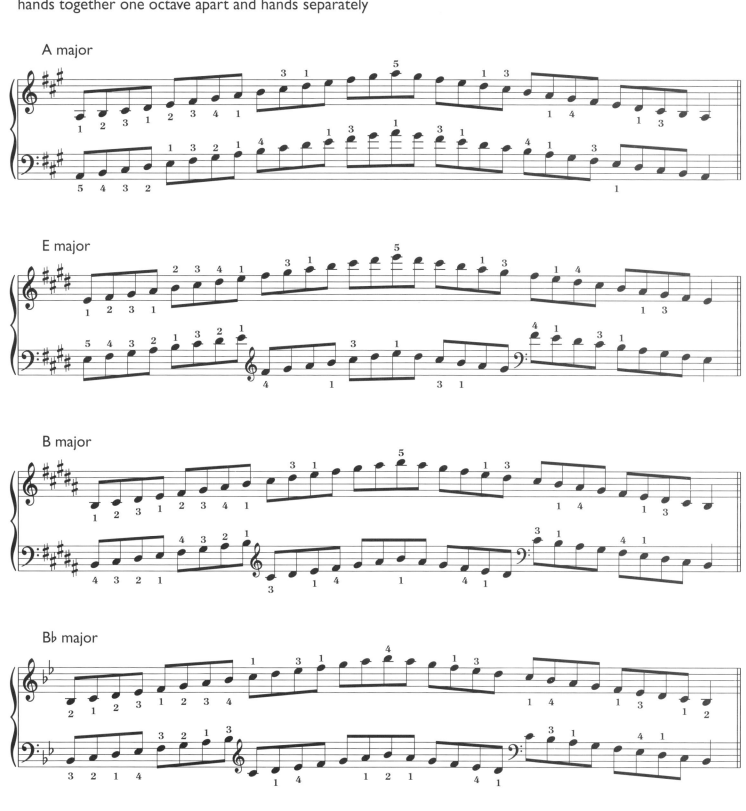

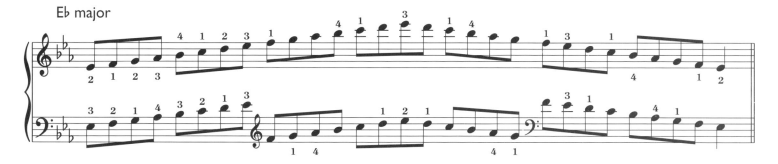

MINOR SCALES

(in melodic *or* harmonic form at candidate's choice)
hands together one octave apart and hands separately

two octaves ♩ = 80

B minor melodic

G minor melodic

C minor melodic

or

B minor harmonic

G minor harmonic

C minor harmonic

AB 3404

CONTRARY-MOTION SCALES

hands together beginning on the key-note (unison)

two octaves ♩ = 80

A major

A minor harmonic

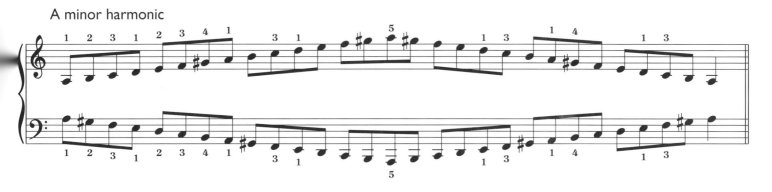

CHROMATIC SCALES

hands separately

two octaves ♩ = 80

beginning on A♭

beginning on C

ARPEGGIOS

hands together one octave apart

two octaves ♩ = 69

hands separately

Music origination by Barnes Music Engraving, East Sussex
Printed in England by Caligraving Ltd, Thetford, Norfolk

CONTRARY-MOTION SCALES

hands together beginning on the key-note (unison)

A major

A minor harmonic

CHROMATIC SCALES

hands separately

beginning on A♭

beginning on C

ARPEGGIOS

hands together one octave apart

A major
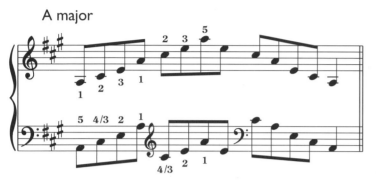

G minor

hands separately

E major

B major

Bb major

Eb major
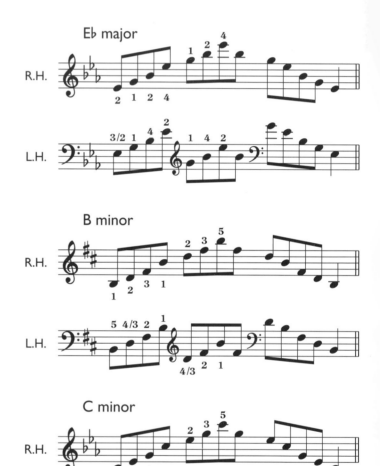

B minor

C minor

Music origination by Barnes Music Engraving, East Sussex
Printed in England by Caligraving Ltd, Thetford, Norfolk